No Frontiers

THE JIMMY MacCARTHY SONGBOOK

Music Setting • John Canning
Cover Design • Temple of Design
Cover Photo • Pat Egan Promotions

The publishers wish to thank the artists and management
for use of photographs on centre pages.

Order No. 1344
ISBN No. 1 85720 124 8

Exclusive Distributors:

Walton Manufacturing Co. Ltd.
Unit 6A, Rosemount Park Drive, Rosemount Business Park,
Ballycoolin Road, Dublin 11, Ireland

Music Sales Limited, Distribution Centre,
Newmarket Road, Bury St. Edmunds, Suffolk IPB 3YB, England

Printed in Ireland by ColourBooks Ltd.

1 3 5 7 9 0 8 6 4 2

CONTENTS

No Frontiers

Words and Music by Jimmy MacCarthy

If life is a ri-ver, your heart is a boat, And just like a wa-ter ba-by, born to float, And if life is the wild wind, that blows way on high, Then your heart is, A-mel-ia,

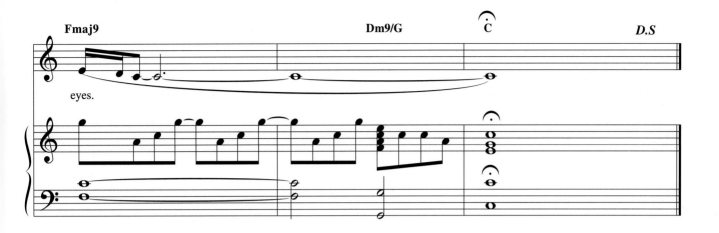

eyes.

And if life is a barroom in which we must wait
Round the man with his fingers on the ivory gates,
Where we sing until dawn of our fears and our fates,
And we stack all the dead men in self-addressed crates,

If your life is a rough bed of brambles and nails,
And your spirit's a slave to man's whips and man's jails,
And you thirst and you hunger for justice and right,
Then your heart is the pure flame of man's constant night,

In your eyes faint as the singing of a lark,
That somehow this dark night feels warmer for the spark,
Warmer for the spark,
To hold us till the day when fear will lose its grip,
And heaven has its way,
And heaven has its way,
When all will harmonise
And know what's in our hearts,
The dream will realise
Heaven knows no frontiers,
And I've seen heaven in your eyes.

Katie

Words and music by Jimmy MacCarthy

Tumb - ling curls of green, By the stained glass stream - ing light. And a yel - low col - oured lamp - shade Used to keep us up all night. The smile up - on your face,

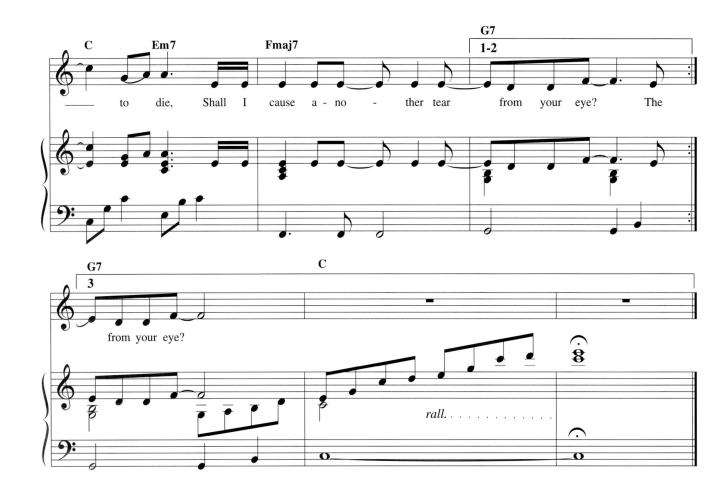

The mirror that won't talk
And your nightgown on the door
The old pedal Singer
Just don't sing no more.
You can roll the reels for hours
From the movie of this book,
It's a question mark on this heart of mine
Sends an elder back to look.

CHORUS

Now I'm looking through a tunnel
Back into the room,
With the genius of a druid
When the sunlight floods the tomb.
And I'm never going back there,
I couldn't anyway,
And though I made the great escape,
I never got away.

CHORUS

A Hard Man to Follow

Words and music by Jimmy MacCarthy

I've been to the moon with the queen of the night, Circ-led the sun and main-tained my sight, I've been to the deep with the dol-phin to play, Be-neath the gol-den bough, with Bud-dha to pray, And we sang

I've ridden on the back of a magical steed,
A dancer reborn, messiah indeed.
And once I did live in a biblical time,
Been to a feast, seen water turned wine.

CHORUS

Sure I'm a hard man to follow, etc.

13

ANCIENT RAIN

Words and music by Jimmy MacCarthy

The witch was clean pushed off my knee, by one born one day after me,
And we went home with lock and key, she left me in the morning.
I slept on till one o'clock and walked out like a concrete block,
I drank some whiskey and I drank it hot on the first day of winter.

Chorus

The summer joy is surely gone, when every clock the hour had on.
Last night we massed and merry made, under the full moon madness played.
See these demons taunt in pagan time, past and present now in rhyme,
Two hands that squeeze my life away, on this the holy All Saints' Day.

Chorus

MYSTIC LIPSTICK

Words and music by Jimmy MacCarthy

She wears mys-tic lip-stick, she wears stones and bones,

She tells myth and leg-end, she sings rock and roll.

She wears chains of bon - dage, she wears wings of hope,

She wears the gown of plen - ty, and still it's hard to cope.

Chorus

Chroí ó mo chroí, your heart is break - ing, Your

eyes are red, your song is blue, Your

And though they feed on what hurts you

To sing the book of your heart,

Oh sweet Black Rose, how they've loved you, And it's hard to, but

they do, Éi - re, they do.

21

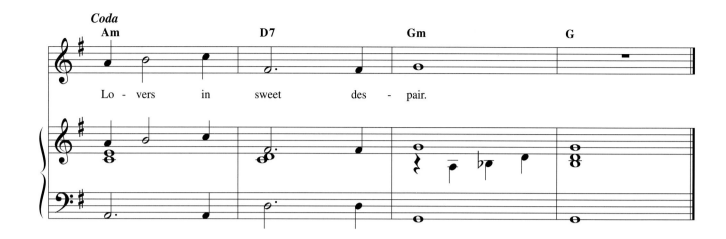

She keeps fools for counsel, she keeps the wig and gown,

The cloth and the bloody warfare, the stars and stripes and crown.

And still we pray for a better day now, God willing it's for the best,

But I've just seen the harp on the penny with a dollar on her naked breast.

CHORUS (twice)

RIDE ON

Words and music by Jimmy MacCarthy

I could ne - ver go with you no mat-ter how I want-ed to.

Chorus

Ride on, see you,

I could ne - ver go with you no mat-ter how I want-ed to.

Ride on,

24

see you, I could ne - ver go with you no mat- ter how I
want- ed to, no mat- ter how I want- ed to,

When you ride into the night without a trace behind,

Run the claw along my gut one last time,

I'll turn to face an empty space where you used to lie,

And smile for the spark that lights the night through the teardrop in my eye.

CHORUS

MISSING YOU

Words and music by Jimmy MacCarthy

To where you're a Pad - dy, and where you're a
Mick, Not much use at all bar stack - ing the
brick. And your mate was a spade and he car - ried the
hod, Two old heav - y hors - es heav - i - ly

Who did you murder, and are you a spy?
I'm just fond of a drink, helps me laugh, helps me cry.
I took to the port for a permanent high,
Now I laugh a lot less and I'll cry till I die.

Now the summer is fine but the winter's a fridge,
Wrapped up in old cardboard under Charing Cross bridge,
And I'll never go home, it's because of the shame,
Of a misfit's reflection in a shop window pane.

So all you young people take an advice,
Before crossing the ocean you'd better think twice,
'Cause you can't live without love, without love alone,
Here's the proof 'round the West End in the nobody zone,

CHORUS

THE CONTENDER

Words and music by Jimmy MacCarthy

When I was young and I was in my day, Sure I'd steal what wom-an's heart there was a-way, And I'd sing in-to the dawn - ing song a-

blaze in-to the mor - ning, Long be-fore I was the man you see to-day. I

2-3 G **Chorus** Em Am D7 G

Fine But there in the mir - ror on the wall

Am Dsus4 D Em Am

I see the dream is fad - ing. From the con - ten - der to

D G F

the brawl, The ring, the rose, the mat - a - dor

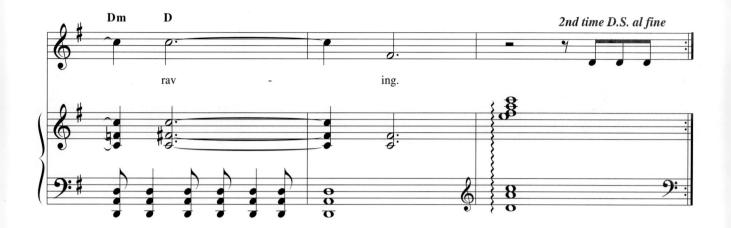

2nd time D.S. al fine

rav - ing.

I was born beneath a star that promised all,
I could have lived my life between Cork, Cobh and Youghal.
But the wheel of fortune took me, from the highest point she shook me,
By the bottle live, by the bottle I shall fall.

CHORUS

And when I die I'll die a drunk down on the street,
He will count me out to ten and clear defeat.
Wrap the starry plough around me, let the piper's air resound me,
And there I'll rest until the lord of love I'll meet.

CHORUS

Wrap the starry plough around me, let the piper's air resound me,
And there I'll rest until the lord of love I'll meet.

adam at the window the highest point ancient rain the
the window the highest poi
point ancient rain th
Katie
wonder child
missing
low the highest po
est point ancient
the contender

Bright Blue Rose

Words and music by Jimmy MacCarthy

I skimmed a-cross Black-wa-ter With - out once sub-mer - ging On- to the banks of an ur-ban mor - ning, That hun - gers first light Much, much more Than moun - tains e - ver do. And she, like a ghost be - side me,

life e - ter - nal - ly.

One bright blue rose out - lives all those, Two thou - sand years and still it goes, To

pon - der his death, and his life e - ter - nal - ly.

Neidín

Words and music by Jimmy MacCarthy

As I leave be-hind Nei-dín, It's like pur-ple splashed on green. My soul is strange-ly fed, Through the wind-ing hills a-head. And she plays a me-lo-dy,

And we wind and climb and fall
Like the greatest waltz of all,
Float across the floor,
Her sweet breath outside the door,
And it's time that I was gone
'Cross the silver tear.

CHORUS

As I leave behind Neidín
In the hall where we have been,
Rhododendrons in her hair,
In the mountain scented air.
I still feel her spirit song
'Cross the silver tear.

CHORUS

ADAM AT THE WINDOW

Words and music by Jimmy MacCarthy

A-dam's at the win-dow, star-ing at the ap-ple trees on fire,

Wait-ing for the wind-fall that brings the smile of kings and their de-

sire. Door blows in be-hind him, a

flor-al pat-tern sum-mer dress so gay, Burn-ing in the sun-light, too

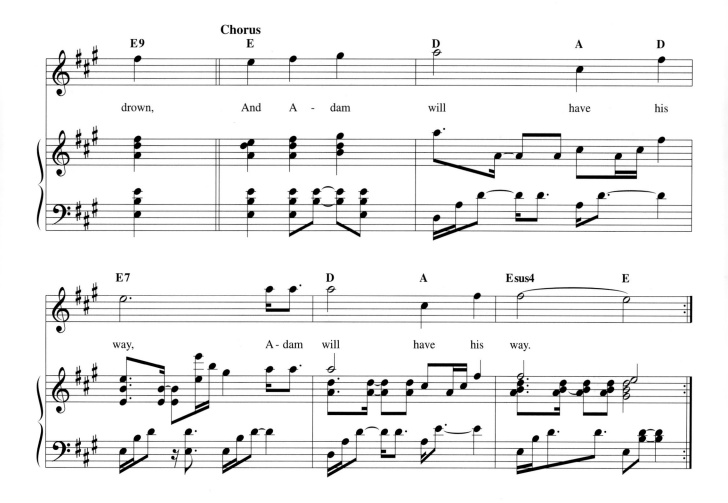

Chorus

drown, And A-dam will have his way, A-dam will have his way.

Adam's on the island, living in the land of love.

Shadows lurk around him, drunk on the royal jelly of pure love.

Full and ripe the fruit hang, for when the prince arrives he will want more,

And more and more he'll drink from the canvas cup,

The son of a swan will then lose his plume array,

And he will wear a new age suit and haunt the joints in town,

And play a silver magic flute and call his lover down,

And call his lover down,

CHORUS

Adam's at the easel, painting in the wrinkles and the grey,

Waiting for November, easy with the darkness and the day.

Smiles a tear of gladness and Adam's at the window once again.

He's burning in the sunlight, too late to wait,

For darkness won't delay, to steal her cherry lips away,

For while the careless tongues of sunlight slowly trickle down,

The curve of hips, her fingertips in kissing sips we drown,

In kissing sips we drown,

CHORUS

43

THE SKY ROAD

Words and music by Jimmy MacCarthy

Dan-ny's made his mind up, he's leav-ing for A-

me - ri - ca, He's leav-ing for A - me - ri - ca, leav-ing

all of us be-hind. He says there's

no-thing here not drenched in beer and blood and re - tri - bu -

tion, And the wealth dis - tri - bu - tion's been

weigh - ing up - on his mind.

Chorus Em

And he knows that he'll re - gret the leav - ing,

Em/C♯ C

Knows that he will pine for griev - ing For the Sky Road by the

G D

sing - ing sea And all of us be - hind.

Danny looks so lovely working in the fields
Or dancing like a wild one, sparks flying 'round his heels.
But his friends all gone before him, from the sacred ground that bore them,
Where they wonder does she scorn them for giving up the land.

CHORUS:
And they know that they'll regret the leaving,
Know that they will pine for grieving
For the Sky Road by the singing sea
And all of us behind.

Danny's made his mind up, he's leaving for America,
He's leaving for America, leaving all of us behind.

CHORUS

47

THE HIGHEST POINT

Words and music by Jimmy MacCarthy

I was dream-ing of my love, With her hair tied up a-bove, That fair face that lights my soul She must have sto-len it from an an-gel.

We were dan - cing by the sea, Said how she'd been miss - ing me, The sweet - ness of a song set free, A song sung o - ver and o - ver and o - ver.

Still I won - der why I

follow her, and I wonder why I care, As I lift my face up from my hands, a - gain I find her there. She's the dread of my night - mare, she's the love of my life, You see, a dream can be the

Nights in dreams of heaven blue,
Stitched and fused as one we flew,
Till I awoke again and knew
That my heart is always waiting.

CHORUS

On the breeze the spirit muse,
She calls me out and leaves me clues,
She sings sean-nós, and she sings the blues,
And her fool again pushed over.

We were dancing by the sea,
Said how she'd been missing me,
The sweetness of a song set free,
A song sung over and over and over.

CHORUS

We were dancing by the sea,
Said how she'd been missing me,
The sweetness of a song set free,
A song sung over and over and over.

CHORUS

WONDER CHILD

Words and music by Jimmy MacCarthy

This child he means the world to me, there is no more en-chan-ted, A child can take this place of ruin and mag-ic-'lly en-hance it. I see him in a gold-en room with the book of life be-fore him, Strange in-stru-ments up-on his charts and the

This child will build a violin; one will follow the traveller's love,
Another will the bow apply to reach the one above.
I see her in a golden room with the moon and stars about her,
Her simple smile is Heaven's gate with the Queen of all beside her.

CHORUS:

She's your wonder child,

And my dreams come true.

You've searched all your life,

I see her now flying over the universe.

CHORUS (2nd time):

Your wonder child,

And my dreams come true.

You've searched all your life,

I see them now flying over the universe.

THE MAD LADY AND ME

Words and music by Jimmy MacCarthy

She leaned and leaned much closer, and hugged them all goodbye,
Her mother cried, 'Don't go my love', we all must by and by.
A drunken tongue said, 'Leave her off, she'll drive us all crazy.'
She turned around and saw my face, and both of us were she.
And we sang—

CHORUS

Up onto the limestone wall and down the ladder steps,
She threw herself into the stream with a splash of no regrets.
Sidestroke swimming midstream, throwing kisses to the crowd,
And everything was silent, and the sky had not one cloud.
But for—

CHORUS

THE SONG OF THE SINGING HORSEMAN

Words and music by Jimmy MacCarthy

This is a prayer boat, so that it may float on down
To the feet of the Lord, burning bright above confusion,
Rising up with a hallelujah, glory, glory hallelujah.
Begone unholy winds, from hallowed halls call godly friends.

It's the blue light of His holy cross,
It's the white-winged horse,
It's the song of the singing horseman,
For every burdened heart and his own.

Chorus